G000299000

GRADE 2

GRADE 3

a Andante con moto

b Poco Allegro

GRADE 4

GRADE 5

GRADE 6

GRADE 7

a

b

Allegro non tanto

GRADE 8

a

b

Poco Allegro

Printed in England by Caligraving Limited Thetford Norfolk 6:04

A|B|R|S|M
PUBLISHING

**The Associated Board of
the Royal Schools of Music
(Publishing) Limited**

24 Portland Place
London W1B 1LU
United Kingdom

www.abrsmpublishing.co.uk

ISBN 1-85472-387-1